Autism Repo

Susan Louise Peterson

Copyright

Autism
Report Writing

Susan Louise Peterson

Contents

❖

Preface

— ❖ —

Early childhood professionals are swamped with writing reports that discuss children's autism concerns and developmental delays. As professionals have time constraints and an overwhelming amount of educational details, I felt a need to focus this work on hints and suggestions to broaden the professionals' writing style. The book **Autism Report Writing** focuses on different ways to describe a child's participation in the classroom, preschool, daycare and home settings. These valuable autism reports may guide a child's eligibility and education program determination to address each child's specific needs.

One of the most common mistakes made is being to general in reports and not describing each child's personal situations. There are many elements of autism report writing and these elements can include over all information on the child's strengths and weaknesses, preschool progress and how referrals are made. Input is another factor that can be included in reports whether it is from outside sources, teachers, parents or agencies working with the child. As well, the observations of the child are invaluable in writing an autism report to be fully descriptive of the child.

Prologue

❖

This is not my first book on autism, but since I spend an enormous amount of time writing autism reports I wanted to write a book on this topic. When I reflect on my first autism book (**Is My Child Autistic or Delayed**?), I tried to cover topics that applied to both parents and professionals in understanding developmental delays and autism concerns. My second autism book (**Questionable Autism**) focused on the types of questions parents and professionals could ask to better understand autism and gain input from those evaluating or working with the child.

The present book (**Autism Report Writing**) emphasizes the value of using report writing to help guide choices that impact the child's future educational journey. Autism reports cover a wide variety of information from initial concerns for the child to recommendations for specific autism programs or educational planning that meets each child's needs. The journey for many children with autism is complex and these written reports are important in describing the child's intricate nature.

Acknowledgements

❖

I am grateful for all of the professional colleagues I have known over the years and their input on my report writing. Their editorial comments at meetings, brief suggestions in the hallway and personal remarks have all helped me improve and reflect on my report writing style. My professional friends have grown over the years and I will miss many of these colleagues who are now retiring and going on a new journey.

When I first started writing autism books my twin daughters were very young and didn't quite understand their mother's insane passion for writing. However, they took the journey with me even though they were not quite sure what I was doing during those early morning hours. Now that the twins have grown up and are heading to college I hope the twins develop their own individual writing journey as a form of self expression. I wish my daughters the best in the incredible journey they will be taking next year.

I can't forget to thank my wonderful husband, Alan for his unbending support of my writing career. His late night hours helping me with computers and tech work was the support I needed after a hard day as a tired writer working with young children.

Introduction

❖

I never really thought much about writing a book called **Autism Report Writing** until I reflected on how important these reports were in determining a child's autism eligibility for special education. Parents come to school early childhood diagnostic and eligibility centers with lots of ideas about autism. Some of those ideas are misguided and confusing, while some of the parent's ideas are right on target about autism. Written autism reports can address parent concerns and how the child was referred for an autism evaluation.

These written autism reports can address parent concerns and how the child was referred for an autism evaluation. These reports can have value in describing the child's strengths and weaknesses, behavioral responses and the child's focus and understanding of the immediate environment. The topics of communication and social responses can be written to explore the child's skills to maneuver in social situations. Reports can also address the child's compliance and toleration responses. An important component of autism report writing is to make recommendations that will help parents and professionals as they the guide the child's educational planning and become familiar with the specific needs of the child.

CHAPTER 1

❖

The Value of Autism Report Writing

As a school psychologist and early childhood educator I have seen the value of good quality autism reports in explaining a child's characteristics, actions and symptoms. The reports on autism serve many purposes such as understanding the child's progress and presenting the child's strengths and weaknesses. Autism reports are used to make referrals to other agencies or programs that may help the child. A well written and helpful descriptive comment about the child may be a strong factor in the decision making process as to whether a child will receive treatment and services for autism from existing agencies or new programs. Certainly autism reports are used to determine educational eligibility for special education services. As well, autism reports are used to report injuries and accidents that have happened to the child in various settings.

Autism writing and records can be used to explain autism and behavior issues at parent conferences. Reports on autism can explain a child's communication patterns. A written report may be needed to get parent input as concerns are noted and the parent may be asked to sign a written report that the family was informed of a certain concern with the child. A written autism report may explain the child's daycare or academic situation to others evaluating the child. Teacher input autism reports are also needed to see how a child functions and performs in an in a group setting. One of the most important uses of autism report writing is to record the observations of the child to document autism or developmental delay concerns.

Autism Progress Reporting

An autism report can explain the child's progress by identifying his or her strengths and weaknesses. Each unique child will have inner strengths and weaknesses that should be identified as he or she reaches a broader social setting and beginning to have more communications encounters.

Example of Strengths Description

Barbara's strength is that she was observed to remain calm when another nearby student was having a tantrum. She is pleasant in class and calm when demands are placed on her. Barbara was very fussy when she started preschool, but she has made major improvement in handling her emotions and frustration.

Example of Weaknesses Description

Barbara's weakness is in following directions. She can sometimes follow a one step direction, but gets very distracted with two step directions. In a class activity observation, she was able to complete the first part of a two step direction, but then lost focus and engaged in a new activity.

Autism Referral Reporting

The autism report can be used to refer a child for assistance and make a referral to an agency or program. These referrals are absolutely necessary to coordinate services for the child and find the programs and agencies that best meet the child's needs.

Example of Agency Referral

Sharon was referred to the Child ... Agency by an early intervention program that helps children transition to the school district. Sharon completed three months of intervention with weekly visits from a developmental specialist and a speech therapist. Her mother stopped the intervention services due to her swing work schedule and difficulty being home for the intervention services. Sharon's mother is open and receptive to getting services to help Sharon's preschool experience.

Example of Program Referral

Sharon came to the early childhood assessment after completing the six week behavior intervention program through a child protective agency. The behavior intervention program focused on helping children deal with emotions and Sharon's caseworker indicated that she had made improvements from the program.

Autism Eligibility Referral

The autism report can be an eligibility report that determines if a child qualifies to receive special education services. These autism eligibility reports are important and are often transferred from state to state if a child moves to a new area.

Autism Eligibility Determination

Jody demonstrated many types of behaviors that are frequently observed in children with autism. The multidisciplinary team observed autism concerns during the assessment and the parent reported autism characteristics on the checklists and instruments. An additional observation in the home indicated that Jody met the criteria for autism. Jody is eligible under the category of autism according to the state guidelines.

Autism- Not Eligible Determination

Jody's parents reported some autism concerns on checklists, but an in depth home assessment observation revealed that Jody did not meet the educational criteria for autism. Jody has delays in the areas of communication and socialization skills and appears to be eligible in the educational eligibility category of developmental delays.

Autism Behavior Reporting

There are times an autism report or explanation is needed to describe the child's issues to the parent. Sometimes parents are not convinced the child has autism and the report is very important in describing the child autism characteristics and behaviors in social settings.

Example of Autism Behavior Issue

Evan appeared very anxious and clingy to his mother during the assessment. His mother tried to encourage him, but he did not attempt any tasks. The school psychologist tried to warm up Evan with toys and games, but he continually whined and cried throughout the entire assessment. When the testing booklet was placed in front of him, Evan became agitated and at one point attempted to open the door and leave the room.

Example of an Inconsistent Autism Behavior Issue

It was difficult to establish rapport with Evan, but after he warmed up he participated in some activities. When his mother offered him a snack it seemed to calm him down. Some of this participation was inconsistent in the preschool. For example, Evan did not participate in any social interaction activities, but he actively participated in drawing and puzzle activities.

Autism Communication Reporting

Written autism reports can help explain the child's communication patterns. Communication is definitely an important element in looking at autism so communication observations and how the child attempts to reach out to others needs to be described in the reports.

Example of Pragmatic Communication

Ricky said no words during the assessment. He attempted to communicate by shrugging his shoulders when he didn't know the answers to the questions. When his mother asked if he wanted a snack he shook his head side to side to indicate 'no.' He waved good bye to the school psychologist when he left the room.

Example of Social Interaction Communication

Ricky transitioned well from one room to another and started to play with the toys. Suddenly, Ricky became frustrated and started to throw the puzzle pieces. The speech therapist tried to redirect Ricky to a new activity, but he refused. Ricky looked toward his mother and she attempted to comfort him. Once Ricky calmed down, he made eye contact and shared a toy with the speech therapist.

Parent Input Reporting

The parent may be interviewed to gain input on the child's issues. Parents often know their children the best so parent input is extremely important in understanding why the child behaves in a certain way.

Example of Parent Input

Erin's mother reported that Erin really likes the kids in her preschool class and that she socializes well with other children. Her mother indicated that Erin is excited about going to preschool and never cries when she is dropped off at preschool. The only concern her mother brought up is that Erin is nervous and cries when a large toy dinosaur is used for preschool class activities.

Example of Parent Frustration Input

Erin's mother indicated that she is very frustrated when she can't do something. As a result, Erin's frustration turns to worry because she tries to be perfect and is too serious about the small things. Erin gets extremely frustrated when oral language activities are presented because she has a limited vocabulary.

Teacher Input Reporting

There are times teacher input is needed on how a child is performing in a group setting with other children. Preschool teachers can help share important details that a parent may miss when a child is only in the home setting and has limited social interaction.

Example of Telephone Interview with Teacher

A telephone interview was conducted on Feb. 6, 2015 with Ms. Jones (Emily's preschool teacher.) Ms. Jones noted that Emily does well in one-on-one situations, but has difficulty with transitions to group situations. Emily refuses to participate in circle time activities and needs lots of encouragement to join group activities.

Example of Teacher Interview about Child

Emily's preschool teacher participated in the early childhood assessment process. She shared that Emily is frustrated the first few minutes of class and it is difficult to calm her down. However, when Emily is bored, she calls for 'momma' over and over again and starts crying about the time class is over. She appears to have difficulty adapting to separation in the preschool setting.

Academic Situation Reporting

A written autism report can be used to explain a child's unique situation and behavior in an academic setting. Since each academic situation is unique this type of reporting can go in a lot of different directions. Some academic situations are more structured, while other situations put less demands on a child so the written descriptions should explain the child's unique situation.

Example of Academic Setting Report

During center rotations in preschool, Jean was difficult to engage. In the block center, she knocked the blocks off of the table. When she was in the art center she fussed and pushed the writing materials off of the table. The preschool has a structured rotation of centers and students are expected to participate during these center rotations.

Example of Specific Academic Situation

Jean was difficult to engage in circle time activities. She showed little interest in stories and walked away when the other students played a hand clapping game. Although students are not required to participate in all activities, it is noted that Jean has very limited participation in most activities.

Injury Reporting

Most professionals will from time to time have to report an injury they observed during testing or in a preschool setting.

Example of Finger Injury Report

On March 13, 2015 at 8:30a.m.Juan was in the school psychologist's office and opened the office door. When his mother told him to close it, his fingers were briefly pinched in the door. Juan was taken to the front office and given an ice pack for his fingers. Juan stopped crying and completed the morning assessment.

Example of Head Injury Report

Maria ran into the speech therapist's office at approximately 10:30a.m. on April 16th, 2015. Maria was wearing flip flops and upon entering the office she tripped and bumped her head on the edge of the desk. Maria's head was bleeding and she was taken immediately to the school nurse's office where the nurse cleaned the wound and placed a band-aid on it. The assessment was stopped and Maria's mother rescheduled another date to complete the assessment.

Observation Reporting

The professional's observations are often recorded to better explain how the child interacts in various settings and situations. These observations can be valuable in providing additional information to formal testing assessments.

Example of Preschool Observation

Beth's preschool observation occurred on the playground of her preschool center during the morning recess and play activities. Beth was observed to grab a toy from one child. When the teacher's assistant asked her about the toy she stared blankly and did not seem to understand what the assistant was saying to her.

Example of Daycare Observation

A daycare observation was completed on Friday, June 6th, 2015 at an in home daycare center. Four children were observed in the home daycare setting. Beth's daycare teacher indicated that she is easy to care for, responds well to directions and seems to enjoy the other children.

CHAPTER 2

❖

Explaining Autism Concerns

Autism reports will often begin with explaining who is making the autism concern for the child. These concerns will come from a variety of sources. The way the concern is written may impact how it is interpreted by the professionals and parents reading the report. As these reports come from different people they will have a variety of angles in how the child's information is presented. For instance, if a child is in foster care, the foster parent may be expressing the autism concern. Parents and family members often make autism referrals because they spend the most time with the child and know the child's reactions and patterns of behavior in the home setting. Referrals for autism concerns can come from daycare providers and preschool teachers who work with young children in center and learning activities.

Many children who are in the home setting will get autism referrals from early intervention specialists who observe the child's behavior during weekly and monthly visits. Speech and occupational therapists who have had sessions with the child will also point out autism concerns the therapists noticed in working with the child. During educational evaluations a multidisciplinary team may notice autism concerns. In addition, physicians may either make a medical diagnosis of autism or mention autism concerns in their reports. Phrasing autism concerns in reports can be problematic if the autism concern is too general and not specific enough to describe the child.

Foster Care Autism Concerns

Written Example

The foster parent is sure that Sammy has autism.

Optional Writing Formats

The foster parent expressed concerns for Sammy primarily in the areas of autism and speech.

The foster parent commented that Sammy is difficult to care for and could possibly have autism.

Autism concerns were conveyed by the foster family who have cared for Sammy for two years.

The foster parents noted that Sammy ignores most requests and they have concerns he may have autism.

The foster parent reported that the birth history of Sammy is unknown.

Parent Autism Concerns

Written Example

The parent thinks Annabel may have autism because she tantrums.

Optional Writing Formats

Annabel has severe tantrums and her parent is really concerned she may have autism.

The parent is concerned about autism because Annabel loses her temper too easily.

Annabel's mother is worried she may have autism as she yells frequently and makes high pitched sounds.

The parent mentioned autism concerns because Annabel gets very upset over small things.

Annabel's parent wants to consider some additional testing to see if she may have autism.

Family Member Autism Concerns

Written Example

The relatives think Rita could be autistic

Optional Writing Formats

Rita's caregiver noticed that Rita is extremely shy and could possibly be autistic.

Rita's family noticed that she is always rocking back and forth and they have concerns about autism.

Rita's aunt has autism concerns because she whirls and spins in circles for long periods of time.

Rita's grandmother reported that Rita spins the car wheels often and she is concerned about autism.

Rita's uncle reported some autism concerns related to playing repetitively with objects.

Teacher Autism Concerns

Written Example

The teacher mentioned that Kyle may have autism.

Optional Writing Formats

The teacher noted that Kyle is very destructive with toys and that autism may be a possibility.

The teacher observed that Kyle does not respond to his name and that she has autism concerns.

Kyle is often standoffish with the other children and his teacher commented that it might be autism.

The teacher noticed that Kyle did not interact with the other children and the possibility of autism concerned him.

Kyle's teacher noticed that he never joins any group activities.

Daycare Autism Concerns

Written Example

The daycare director is sure that Donna has autism and needs help.

Optional Writing Formats

The daycare staff mentioned that Donna may have autism because she will not show toys and interact with staff members.

The director of the daycare center noticed that Donna would not turn around when her name was called and there were autism concerns.

Staff members at the daycare center were concerned with autism because Donna would mumble to herself as she played with toys.

The daycare director spoke with Donnas' mother regarding autism concerns as Donna does not respond to animal sounds.

Donnas' daycare provider noticed that she has some sensory issues and does not play with toys appropriately.

Early Intervention Autism Concerns

Written Example

The early intervention specialist thinks Jeff has autism.

Optional Writing Formats

The early intervention specialist suggested that Jeff may have autism as he turned the lights on and off during a home visit.

Jeff ran out of the front door of his house three times and the early intervention specialist mentioned the possibility of autism to his father.

The early intervention specialist working with Jeff noted autism concerns as he would open and close the door repeatedly during the home visit.

The early intervention specialist who worked with Jeff for one year had autism concerns related to his distant behavior and lack of interaction with people.

Jeff's early intervention specialist mentioned several autism concerns in her report.

Occupational Therapist Autism Concerns

Written Example

The occupational therapist noticed some autism red flags in Josh's behavior.

Optional Writing Formats

The occupational therapist noted autism red flags as Josh did not play with the toys appropriately.

Josh kept spinning the wheels on the toy and the occupational therapist mentioned autism possibilities.

The occupational therapist noted sensory issues related to autism as Josh put many items in his mouth.

Josh's sensitivity to food textures (only eats crunchy foods) was noted as a possible autism characteristic by the occupational therapist.

The occupational therapist documented eating sensitivity issues in her final report.

Speech Therapist Autism Concerns

Written Example

The speech therapist saw some practical issues that indicated Holly may have autism concerns.

Optional Writing Formats

The speech therapist had autism concerns as Holly repeated the word 'no' over and over again in the speech session.

Autism concerns were noted by the speech therapist as Holly used very few social exchanges (only 'hi and bye') in the session.

The speech therapist noticed Holly looked away when her name was called and that was an indication of autism.

Holly only used gestures to get items and the speech therapist pointed out autism characteristics.

Holly's speech therapist had pragmatic communication skills and thought autism was a possibility.

Multidisciplinary Team Autism Concerns

Written Example

The multidisciplinary team noted autism concerns as Patty made no eye contact and only responded to her mother.

Optional Writing Formats

The multidisciplinary team had some autism concerns because Patty repeated everything the nurse asked her in the session.

Autism concerns were noted by the interdisciplinary team when Patty was reluctant to participate in the testing and wandered down the hallway.

Staff members on the multidisciplinary team had autism concerns when Patty would not respond to her name.

The multidisciplinary team noted autism concerns as Patty had minimal eye contact and would only use eye contact with her mother.

The team members noted that Patty had no showing behaviors and only played with toys alone and in the corner of the room.

Physician Autism Concerns

Written Example

The doctor says Antonio may have autism.

Optional Writing Formats

The physician diagnosed Antonio with autism as a medical concern.

The doctor commented that a psycho-educational assessment is needed before a determination of an autism educational eligibility can be made.

Antonio holds a medical diagnosis of autism from Dr. John Doe.

Antonio has no medical diagnosis of autism, but the doctor wants to review the early intervention reports once the autism observation testing has been completed.

Antonio's doctor did not document a medical diagnosis of autism.

CHAPTER 3

❖

Autism Behavior Responses

Chapter three explores the many behaviors that can interfere with understanding autism. As reports are being written there is an emphasis on behavior and emotional issues that can impact a child with autism. The chapter begins with the topics of refusal and aggressive behaviors that some young children experience in preschools, at home and in daycare centers. The topics of frustration, withdrawal and separation responses are discussed as these impact children with autism. Professional observations can include specific observations of the child's refusal behaviors in order to analyze if the child has more purposeful behaviors or unintentional types of behaviors. Specific notes can be included in written reports to record specific incidents of aggressive types of behavior and specific details of the environment, children and adults involved in the situation and the child's responses and reactions to social situations. The autism characteristics can be reported in a time line like report of how the child responds when he or she arrives at school, when specific incidents occurred, how the child interacts or reacts during the school day of scheduled activities, how the child responds when transitions are made and how the child may warm up or get frustrated as the day progress and preschool ends for the day. In report writing, professionals will also address topics such as distraction, nervousness and anxiety as part of autism writing for young children. The chapter ends with a look at how a child with autism may exhibit hesitation and ignoring responses and how professionals write on these topics. These responses can be related to the child's ability to use functional skills or difficulties in learning new skills. The writer has a unique opportunity to explain these very unusual or typical behaviors to get a full picture of the child and share these details in written form.

Refusal Behavior Responses

Written Example

Mia refused to respond to many requests.

Optional Writing Formats

Mia refused to sit in the chair and rolled on the floor.

Mia did not point to body parts or clothing on request and turned away from the teacher.

Mia refused to open her mouth for the speech therapist.

Mia was briefly cooperative and then refused all requests by her teacher.

Mia refused all requests to participate from the school psychologist.

Aggressive Responses

Written Example

Cody is aggressive with other kids.

Optional Writing Formats

Cody becomes aggressive when he wants another child's toy.

Cody was observed on several occasions to be aggressive by invading the space of other children when he was seeking the toys.

Cody will push another child to get the object he desires.

Cody became aggressive when the other children arrived at the center.

Cody continued to be aggressive with other children even after he was given an oral reminder.

Frustration Responses

Written Example

Bobby is frustrated all of the time.

Optional Writing Formats

Bobby seems to get frustrated easily when direct requests are made of him.

Bobby was frustrated when the teacher asked him to sit at the table.

Bobby became frustrated when a new activity was introduced at preschool.

Bobby needed one-on-one attention to deal with his frustrations.

Bobby's frustration was noted and he could anger quickly in even non-threatening situations.

Withdrawn Responses

Written Example

Jayden is withdrawn and shy around other kids.

Optional Writing Formats

Jayden was generally inattentive and withdrawn during circle time.

Jayden was withdrawn as he did not interact with the other children on the playground.

Jayden withdraws during language time and refuses to participate in any activity involving speaking or using words.

When asked to help clean up the play center, Jayden appeared withdrawn and moved to another center.

Jayden would withdraw if a new task was presented at preschool.

Separation Responses

Written Example

Cathy did not separate well from her mother and cried at daycare.

Optional Writing Formats

Cathy has difficulty adapting to change when her mother drops her off at daycare.

Cathy did not separate easily from her mother and had a tantrum when her mother dropped her off at preschool.

Cathy is often insecure and cries for her mother if she is bored or uninterested in the task.

Cathy is easily upset when her mother leaves her at preschool.

Cathy had a severe tantrum if her mother left the room for even a few minutes.

Nervous Responses

Written Example

Mattie is nervous when going to preschool.

Optional Writing Formats

Mattie appears nervous when separating from her grandmother at daycare.

Mattie was uncomfortable and nervous when the older child entered the preschool classroom.

Mattie was nervous when the class changed rooms for the movie.

Mattie has difficulty eating and is nervous when a snack is served.

When dress-up characters entered the preschool, Mattie became very nervous.

Distraction Responses

Written Example

Maria was distracted in the preschool classroom.

Optional Writing Formats

Maria was distracted by the toys, but could easily be redirected.

Maria completes a few activities and then is distracted by her personal interest in the toys.

Maria may listen to a story briefly, but then displays limited interest in a task.

Maria sat at circle time briefly and then was distracted as she walked away from the group.

Maria had a very brief attention span and was distracted often by sounds or music.

Anxiety Responses

Written Example

Aiden was anxious about attending preschool.

Optional Writing Formats

Aiden was fearful, anxious and twisted his hair when a child approached him.

Aiden was anxious and afraid when he saw the medical equipment in the nurse's office.

Aiden seemed anxious when the new toys were brought out in the play center.

Aiden was anxious and chewing on his shirt during circle time.

It was clear Aiden became anxious when the new child entered the circle.

Hesitation Responses

Written Example

Juan was hesitant to participate with the speech therapist.

Optional Writing Formats

Juan was initially shy, but started to warm up and participate after a few minutes.

Juan hesitated when he was in the group activity and did not seem to have the social skills to interact with the other children.

Juan hesitated and did not use functional communication to ask for things from other children.

Juan had difficulty learning a new task and hesitated when asked to imitate an action.

Juan's hesitation was obvious as he hid behind his mother's chair.

Ignoring Responses

Written Example

Derrick ignored the teacher's request to participate in the game.

Optional Writing Formats

Derrick did not respond to his name with four requests from the teacher's assistant.

Derrick did not make eye contact when handed a toy by his caregiver.

Derrick did not respond to a clapping sound in the game.

Derrick did not react or respond to the teacher's request to come to circle time.

Derrick ignored all attempts to participate in play activities from staff members.

CHAPTER 4

❖

Autism Understanding Responses

Autism reports are often focused on examining how a child understands or comprehends various aspects of the environment around him or her. These aspects can include observations of how the child takes direction and how the child responds to redirection and requests. The chapter also explores writing phrases on how the child may comprehend information related to routines and directions. A written report can be focused on whether the child has the ability to complete a task or whether he or she is unable to complete a task. It can describe the child's difficulties in completing an activity and the need for assistance and support to accomplish the activity. On the other hand, the autism report can describe the ease and quickness of how a child completes some tasks and certainly make comments when the child has gifted traits and high functioning cognitive abilities. There can be elements of the written report that comment on the child's struggle to learn new concepts and when the child is frightened to attempt a new task. The report can emphasize if the child has an awareness of the surroundings as he or she is approached with learning activities. These phrases can also be written to describe the child's cognitive understanding of preschool situations as well as the child's abilities to complete a task. The written phrases also explore when a child has inconsistent responses to some requests. Part of the child's understanding can be related to how the child focuses on a task and the way the child gives attention to a particular task. As part of this understanding process the child's response and need for support is examined.

Direction Responses

Written Example

Jennifer did not take direction well from her teacher.

Optional Writing Formats

Jennifer was constantly out of her chair and did not respond when directions were repeated.

Jennifer was unable to stack blocks from oral directions and a demonstration.

Jennifer had difficulty following a direction that was modeled by another student.

Jennifer did not understand oral directions and needed to be given a gesture to come join the group activity.

Jennifer seemed confused and unsure when directions were given.

Redirection Responses

Written Example

Jose needs redirection as he is all over the classroom.

Optional Writing Formats

Jose often wandered to the door and needed redirection to return to his seat.

Jose did not stay in his seat and explored the room needing constant redirection.

Jose needed redirection and it was difficult to gain and sustain his attention.

With constant redirection and reinforcements Jose was able to comply with simple one-step directions.

Jose did not respond well to numerous requests and redirection.

Comprehension Responses

Written Example

Colin does not comprehend what is going on in daycare.

Optional Writing Formats

Colin was very frightened and did not comprehend the fire drill routine.

Colin lacks comprehension of simple classroom routines.

Colin struggles to comprehend language and oral directions.

Colin does not understand or comprehend the preschool routine of changing centers.

Colin had trouble comprehending the pointing activity.

Cognitive Understanding Responses

Written Example

Mike doesn't seem to know what is going on in preschool.

Optional Writing Formats

Mike is still learning to point to an item on request and points to many things with uncertainty.

Mike did not understand the directions of the card matching activity and put the card in his mouth.

Mike put the pencil in his mouth and did not understand how to hold the pencil.

Mike briefly participated in story time, but had a lack of understanding of how to look at pictures in a book.

Mike did not understand how to clap his hands in the group activity.

Ability Responses

Written Example

Jill has the ability to do many things.

Optional Writing Formats

Jill completed each task to the best of her ability.

Jill has limited motor ability when using her left hand, but is very adaptive with her right hand.

Jill has the ability to take a few steps if she is supported by an adult.

Jill attempted all activities presented to her as best she could.

Jill has strong cognitive abilities and can complete many tasks quickly.

Inconsistent Responses

Written Example

Marcos responds sometimes to his teacher's requests and other times may not respond.

Optional Writing Formats

Marcos can follow simple commands like 'sit down,' but it inconsistent with other requests.

Marcos can follow a simple one-step direction like 'get your coat,' but has a harder time and is inconsistent with two step directions.

Marcos can name some colors, but at other times appears inconsistent in naming colors.

Marcos pointed correctly to one animal, but at other times pointed to many animals and was unsure of his responses.

Marcos is inconsistent in his responses to questions about body parts.

Focus Responses

Written Example

Mark does not focus on the preschool activities.

Optional Writing Formats

Mark roamed the preschool classroom for his items of interest, rather than coming to the table activity.

Mark had trouble focusing on the book being read in small group and crawled under the table.

Mark seemed inattentive as he was looking at the toy dinosaurs when the teacher read the story.

Mark was unaware when the teacher called his name and did not respond until the third time the teacher called for him.

Mark had difficulty remaining focused on the apple activity.

Attention to Task Responses

Written Example

Joe left his chair at the desk when asked to draw a picture.

Optional Writing Formats

Joe marked on the paper briefly and then he quickly lost interest in working on the writing task.

Joe was observed to get out of his chair on several occasions and it was difficult to sustain his attention.

Joe was mildly distractible as he left the writing center to access the toy center.

Joe had difficulty sitting and attending to the writing activity.

Joe's involvement in the task was limited because of his short attention span.

Support Responses

Written Example

Nelly needs support with everything.

Optional Writing Formats

Nelly needs additional support when going upstairs to board the bus and must be supervised as she is a runner.

Nelly is receptive to support and help when she falls down.

Nelly needs help and support to verbally express her needs.

Nelly would benefit from adaptive devices to help her communicate in the educational setting.

Nelly needs extra support as she struggles to make new friends at preschool.

Observing Responses

Written Example

Tony only observes children and does not participate in anything.

Optional Writing Formats

Tony only observes other children playing and will not join in play activities with them.

Tony was noted to observe his infant sister trying to reach for the puzzle, but he did not play with the puzzle.

Tony struggled to adapt to the new play center and was observed to move away from the toys.

Tony was observed to move and turn in circles as he lacked an understanding of the circle time activity.

Tony was observing the butterfly, but totally ignored the other children.

CHAPTER 5

❖

Autism Communication Responses

Communication is such an important part of writing autism reports. It is a broad area that encompasses many elements of each individual child's communication style. For instance, there are ways to explain how a child uses pointing responses to communicate his or her wants and needs and indicating active responses, delayed response or simply a lack of participation when pointing to items. The child may also be struggling with naming responses related to objects and pictures. The professional can write about the child's attempts to communicate, the child's limited ability to name objects or a child who has confidence to name and attempt to name items. Part of communication also focuses on the child's nonverbal responses as well as gestures and eye contact to communicate. A written report can examine the child's total avoidance of eye contact, limited eye contact or when the child looks in the direction of the speaker. The communication skills in a child's development can be related to how the child responds to language activities and explore if the child coordinates eye contact with the use of language. These communication responses can be focused on listening responses as well as how the child imitates responses, requests items, makes choices and answers the requests of others. There can be detailed written observations when a child appears not to listen or only partially listens to directions. There can be lots of descriptions of how a child imitates responses, tasks, sounds and words to follow a simple request or direction. A report can show how a picture of how a child communicates to requests with refusals or attempts or makes choices in the preschool setting. A detailed autism report can be more powerful if it has a nice overview of the child's communication strengths and weaknesses.

Pointing Responses

Written Example

Paul will not point to items when asked by his teacher.

Optional Writing Formats

Paul would not participate in a pointing task or point on request.

The lack of a pointing response was noted when Paul turned away from the testing manual.

Paul did not respond when asked to point to body parts on the teddy bear picture.

Paul is still learning to point to a single item there are numerous items on a page.

Paul was unable to point to a picture even after a demonstration.

Naming Responses

Written Example

Jose did not name the objects.

Optional Writing Formats

Jose did not name objects, but made sounds and babbled in an attempt to make his wants and needs known.

Jose was unable to name the toy he wanted, but threw a block at the toy.

Jose could not name the picture in the booklet, but pointed to the correct picture.

Jose has a limited naming vocabulary and mostly gestured and pointed to the desired object.

Jose tried to name the object, but no words were heard.

Eye Contact Responses

Written Example

Tom did not make eye contact with the other child.

Optional Writing Formats

Tom's eye contact was very limited and brief with his friends.

Tom frequently avoided eye contact with his teacher.

Tom looked away quickly and only made eye contact for a few seconds.

Tom looked in the direction of the teacher for only a brief moment.

Tom made 'fleeting' eye contact as he left the room.

Nonverbal Responses

Written Example

Renee used no words in class.

Optional Writing Formats

Renee shrugged her shoulders when she didn't know the answer.

Renee suddenly stopped talking after the new teacher arrived.

Renee was observed to point to objects, but her vocabulary consists of only one word "momma.'

Renee would jump up and down when she wanted something and did not use words to request items.

Renee has stronger nonverbal communication and a weakness in her verbal communication.

Language Activity Responses

Written Example

Teri avoided the learning activities that involved language.

Optional Writing Formats

Teri did not coordinate eye contact with the picture naming activity.

Teri had an upset facial expression when the children started a poem activity.

Teri did not speak any words and his activity participation was limited to playing with dinosaurs in the toy center.

Teri did not participate in the jumping activity because he did not understand the oral directions.

Teri refused to participate in all language activities.

Listening Responses

Written Example

Jose doesn't listen to directions in the play center.

Optional Writing Formats

Jose appears not to listen and did not respond verbally to any 'yes and no' questions.

Jose does not look at his teacher when she gives instructions and has trouble listening and following directions.

Jose often listens to part of the direction as he may follow the first part of a two step direction.

Jose does not listen when someone is speaking to him for a short period of time.

Jose appears not to listen to parent requests and does things on his own terms.

Imitation Responses

Written Example

Bill has difficulty imitating a request.

Optional Writing Formats

Bill did not imitate motor tasks such as raising his arm or touching his toes.

Bill's teacher presented animal sounds and he was unable to imitate any sounds.

Bill showed no interest in the block testing materials and would not stack the blocks from a demonstration.

Bill had difficulty understanding language and was unable to imitate words on request.

Bill could not imitate a hand gesture with a demonstration.

Request Responses

Written Example

Mary did not respond to the request.

Optional Writing Formats

Mary yelled 'no' at the request to pick up the toys.

Mary threw the toy when a cleanup request was made by her teacher.

Mary refused the request to come to the table as she was distracted by the toys.

Mary needs a demonstration to complete a task and will ignore oral requests.

Mary seemed uninterested and did not follow the request.

Choice Responses

Written Example

Summer has trouble making choices.

Optional Writing Formats

The object was placed out of reach, but in a visible location so Summer could choose a favorite toy.

Summer selected one of two pictures to indicate her desired center activity.

Summer made a choice when a sticker incentive was given to her.

The teacher held up a ball and a block and Summer pointed to the ball to make her choice.

Summer did not seem to understand how to make a choice between the two pictures.

Answering Responses

Written Example

Jordan does not answer questions from his teacher.

Optional Writing Formats

Jordan did not turn toward his teacher and would not answer her when she asked his name.

When asked a question, Jordan responded with a humming sound.

When asked which toy he wanted, Jordan took his parent's hand to the object.

Jordan did not utilize any words or answer simple questions.

Jordan's answer was unclear and hard to understand.

CHAPTER 6

❖

Autism Social Responses

The realm of autism report writing would definitely include information related to the child's social responses. The child may be struggling socially in a way that he or she has limited participation in preschool activities as well as infrequent and inconsistent responses to social activities. For example, a report can be a description of a clingy child who is very frustrated and has limited participation in the social setting. If a child is exhibiting infrequent participation or responses there may be a need to give a written description of when and how often the child participates in an activity. There may also be a need to write about the types of activities the child participates in as well the types of activities that the child avoids or walks away from in the early childhood home or preschool setting. The social realm definitely looks at how the child initiates, responds and participates in play experiences. These social play experience writings may focus on how the child develops friendships and how cooperation is part of this social interaction experience. The social responses of the child are quickly noticed when the child is placed in a social environment with other children and adults. The child may become involved in social exchanges with other children and these often turn into turn taking activities. Professionals will gain plenty of experience writing about these exchanges between children and which children participate, initiate or withdraw during these exchanges. Professionals in the classroom will notice the amount of encouragement a child needs to participate in the social environment and the ease or difficulty in which the child can function in the social environment.

Limited Participation Responses

Written Example

Kim hardly participates in the daycare activities.

Optional Writing Formats

Kim had limited participation in the play routine and only showed one item to another child.

Kim would only participate in activities that involved books.

Kim was frustrated and only had limited participation in puzzle activities.

Kim was clingy to her father and had limited participation in all of the days' activities.

Kim only participated in the playground activities and avoided all of the other activities.

Infrequent Responses

Written Example

Javier participates infrequently in the class activities.

Optional Writing Formats

Javier did not initiate interaction and had infrequent joint attention.

Javier's class participation was infrequent and he tended to move away from the other children.

Javier's eye contact was very infrequent and was only made with a familiar person (mom.)

Javier's engagement in the block center was infrequent and inconsistent.

Javier played infrequently with the other children.

Initiation Responses

Written Example

Beth does not initiate any activities at preschool.

Optional Writing Formats

Beth did not invite others to join in the block activity.

Beth is still learning to use a social greeting like 'hi or bye' to initiate or end a social interaction.

Beth does not initiate sharing skills in the play area and tends to keep toys to herself.

Beth did not self initiate any activities and had to be asked to join in all activities.

Beth was sleeping and unable to initiate any social responses during the session.

Play Responses

Written Example

Javier does not play well at preschool.

Optional Writing Formats

Javier does not seek out other children in preschool to play interactive games.

Javier seldom initiates play with other children in the preschool setting.

Javier often plays alone and does not choose to join in group play activities.

Javier does not understand how to share toys in play exchanges.

Javier had limited play experiences as he entered preschool.

Friendship Responses

Written Example

Leslie had difficulty making friends at preschool.

Optional Writing Formats

Leslie will not approach the other children and will shy away from friendships.

Leslie has not developed any friendships at the daycare.

Leslie has not made friendships and is unaware of the other children around her.

Leslie has a difficult time approaching other children to interact and develop friendships.

Leslie tries to reach out to others, but has some difficulty making friends.

Cooperation Responses

Written Example

Mike was not cooperative in the testing session.

Optional Writing Formats

Mike was cooperative for a brief moment and then was distracted by other items in the room.

Mike followed directions for a few minutes and then become uncooperative and frustrated.

Mike was uncooperative and started to be demanding and forceful with the toys.

Mike was cooperative for some activities, but at other times exhibited refusal behaviors.

Mike only cooperated for a brief moment before he fell asleep.

Turn Taking Responses

Written Example

John had problems taking turns on the playground.

Optional Writing Formats

John takes turns when the class is lined up for water, but not when he is on the playground.

John takes turns in structured situations, but has difficulty taking turns in less structured activities.

John waits for a prompt and then takes his turn.

John cries and does not want the other students to have a turn holding the toys.

John does not understand how to take turns in group settings.

Social Exchange Responses

Written Example

Zoey won't make social exchanges in preschool.

Optional Writing Formats

Zoey will play with toys, but is not yet participating in social exchanges.

Zoey will take turns in non-verbal exchanges, but is not taking turns in verbal exchanges.

Zoey does not understand social exchanges when another child is offered a turn to play with her toy.

Social exchanges are difficult for Zoey in the preschool environment as she will not take turns.

Zoey refused all attempts to make social exchanges with peers.

Encouragement Responses

Written Example

Amy needed more encouragement than the other children.

Optional Writing Formats

Amy needed encouragement to make a choice between the toys.

Amy needed to be asked to pick up the toys and only participated after she was given a directive.

Amy seemed reluctant to try new things and needed extensive encouragement to attempt a task.

Amy needed extra reinforcement and encouragement to line up with the class.

Amy appears to need a strong amount of encouragement to participate in most tasks.

Engagement Responses

Written Example

Kayla had trouble engaging in the classroom activities.

Optional Writing Formats

Kayla did not engage in pretend play activities.

Kayla had trouble taking cues from other students and only engaged in self-directed play.

It was difficult to engage Kayla in the activities and sustain her attention.

Kayla would not engage with other people and would cry when approached by others.

Kayla never engaged in the puppet activity with the other children and preferred to play alone.

CHAPTER 7

❖

Autism Compliance Responses

The topic of compliance is a part of describing a child's autism characteristics. This compliance may include writing about how compliant or noncompliant the child is when asked to participate in a variety of tasks. This may include the child's responses as he or she is accessing the materials in the room as well as monitoring the child for support and task completion. Writings can include a look at the child's need for adaptive equipment as well as the child's ability level to access and use preschool classroom materials. The amount of monitoring a child will need in an educational setting can be discussed with a description of the child and ideas about needed support from staff and caretakers. Compliance as a writing topic may include comments on the child's effort and motivation on tasks as well as the child's resistive responses to some tasks. Task completion can be another descriptive writing topic and these observations can be recorded as the child is observed attempting a variety of tasks to explore personal interest, motivation, skills and the ability level of the child. In particular, a child with autism concerns may have delayed responses when approached with social and communication requests. The child's compliance may include writing about inconsistent behaviors the child is observed having in the preschool setting routines. As well, part of compliance involves the child's activity level as he or she participates with groups of children. There is definitely a need to write about compliance when explaining a child's autism concerns and these written comments can certainly help a multidisciplinary team make educational decisions for the child's future.

Compliance Responses

Written Example

Jack is totally noncompliant at daycare.

Optional Writing Formats

Jack would complete some activities and then became noncompliant as he abruptly shut down without any further effort on the task.

Jack was noncompliant with most requests from his teacher.

Jack was only noncompliant when asked to join group activities.

Jack would not give oral responses and became noncompliant when asked a question.

Jack has severe noncompliant behavior that interferes with his class participation.

Access Responses

Written Example

Nick could not access the equipment in the room.

Optional Writing Formats

Nick demonstrated a slow response as he accessed the toy.

Nick accessed some of the educational materials placed on the table.

Nick needs adaptive equipment to access the learning materials.

Nick accessed the educational equipment to the best of his ability.

Nick did not understand how to access the materials in the classroom.

Monitor Responses

Written Example

Eddie needs constant monitoring in preschool.

Optional Writing Formats

Eddie's speech sounds need to be monitored once he uses more language.

Eddie needs to be monitored for safety as he is a runner.

Eddie tends to stuff his mouth and needs to be monitored in relation to chewing and swallowing.

Eddie needs to be monitored when sitting in a chair as he was observed to fall out of his seat.

Eddie is unaware of his surroundings and needs to be monitored in all settings.

Task Completion Responses

Written Example

Mimi never completes tasks at preschool.

Optional Writing Formats

Mimi will not complete a task unless the request is repeated several times before she attempts the task.

Mimi would turn away from the requested task after a few minutes into the task.

Mimi cried and walked away from the table when the teacher introduced a new activity.

Mimi refused to complete the task and moved to her preferred interest in the toy center.

Mimi had difficulty completing even one task when given a demonstration.

Effort Responses

Written Example

Ellie did not make a good effort in the activity.

Optional Writing Formats

Ellie make a sincere effort when an easy task was given, but turned away from difficult tasks.

Ellie made the best effort she could on each task presented to her.

Ellie's effort was limited as she refused all attempts to complete a direct task.

It was hard to determine Ellie's true effort as she had significant refusal behaviors on all requested tasks.

Ellie made a good effort, but still had trouble comprehending the task.

Motivation Responses

Written Example

Lee was not motivated to participate in the preschool activities.

Optional Writing Formats

Lee's motivation was limited as she resisted the evaluation by covering her ears.

Lee was not motivated to complete the task as she whined and cried throughout the coloring activity.

Lee's motivation was impacted by her tantrum behavior.

Lee's motivation to complete the puzzle was hampered when she became frustrated and agitated.

Lee did not seem motivated as he appeared very tired.

Resistive Responses

Written Example

Helen was very resistive in movement activities.

Optional Writing Formats

Helen resisted moving when the toy was placed in her arms.

Helen was resistive when asked to share the toy.

Helen engaged in some activities, but resisted activities involving other children.

Helen resisted hand over hand assistance, but was observed to use her mother's hand to activate a small toy.

Helen is resistive when new learning activities are introduced.

Delayed Responses

Written Example

Emily delays her responses to questions from the teacher.

Optional Writing Formats

Emily had a serious look on her face as she slowly answered the teacher's question.

Emily was delayed in interacting with her teacher and would not interact until the teacher asked a question.

Emily's response was delayed as she made sure she answered the teacher's question correctly.

Emily had difficulty with oral questions and delayed answers until she had the right words.

Emily was observed to have a delayed response when the clean up bell was ringing.

Inconsistent Routine Responses

Written Example

Page gets upset when some routines are changed.

Optional Writing Formats

Page was observed to tantrum when the class changed to different centers.

Page would participate in the circle time routine, but had difficulty with the lunch procedures.

Page responded with crying when a substitute teacher changed the classroom routine.

Page needed assistance with some toileting routines as she will not speak or indicate when soiled.

Page does not respond well to slight changes in routines.

Activity Level Responses

Written Example

Steve's activity level was disturbing.

Optional Writing Formats

Steve was very distractible and had a very high activity level.

Motor tasks were difficult for Steve because of his slow activity level.

Steve was difficult to engage in the circle time game due to his high activity level.

Steve's activity level was low as kept laying his head on the desk to rest.

It was difficult to observe Steve's activity level as he was very tired.

CHAPTER 8

❖

Autism Toleration Responses

Professional will often write and examine toleration issues in children. This helps those reading the report understand how much the child tolerated or what types of frustration the child is experiencing. These toleration topics can involve how the child transitions from one activity to another as well as how the child selectively participates in activities. General information can be explained to understand how absorbed the child is and how easily the child is startled by the environment and surroundings. The child's toleration for working with materials as well as the child's inappropriate responses to situations can be recorded in written forms. The written autism reports may include discussions of the child's repetitive responses when involved with different materials in the classroom. These repetitive responses can be described when the child is alone spinning a toy or in a situation that is annoying others as the child turns the lights on and off numerous times with reactions and comments from staff and students. Another aspect of toleration involves how the child responds to changing routines in the environment and working with different people in various situations. Routine and transition changes may occur in a broad range of settings. There are transitions made in small group settings and centers as well as in the bigger group classroom environment and a school transition setting with a very large group of children. The child's use of boundaries is part of toleration and can describe many of the child's frustration and difficulties in the preschool or daycare setting. Toleration issues are great to include in written autism reports as they provide a broad description of the child.

Toleration Responses

Written Example

Kay did not tolerate the classroom activities.

Optional Writing Formats

Kay tolerated some of the staff to help her, but at other times became uncooperative and did not tolerate certain staff members.

Kay tolerated the nurse as she repositioned her on the mat, but was frustrated when the physical therapist moved her.

Kay was very tolerant of being handled by the staff until a room change was made.

Kay tolerated the new walker with ease, but was soon frustrated by the loud noise.

Kay did not tolerate the noise when the door closed.

Transition Responses

Written Example

Billy did not transition well in class.

Optional Writing Formats

Billy was unable to line up with the other students as they were leaving the classroom.

Billy is dependent on others for support and needs assistance with all transitions.

Billy did not consistently follow classroom routines and was often in the corner by himself.

Billy did not participate with the class as they moved from the classroom to the playground..

Billy is improving on his transitions during circle time.

Selective Responses

Written Example

Erin gets upset when asked to do certain things.

Optional Writing Formats

Erin participated in the bubble activity, but refused all other tasks.

Erin only participated by pointing to one toy she wanted on the shelf.

Erin's participation was limited to only the block activity.

Erin briefly participated in the puppet activity and then shut down when all the other games and activities were presented.

Erin is very selective and only occasionally participates in activities.

Self-Absorbed Responses

Written Example

Alicia seems self-absorbed in her own world.

Optional Writing Formats

Alicia was alert, but appeared self-absorbed when she was playing with the teddy bear.

Alicia was not responsive to sit at the table and play with the toy as she was self-absorbed by her doll.

Alicia was so self-absorbed with the ball that she did not acknowledge the speech therapist.

Alicia mumbled to herself and was so self-absorbed that she made no eye contact with the other children.

Alicia was observed to be self-absorbed and unaware of her surroundings.

Startle Responses

Written Example

Lois was startled by all the toys in the center.

Optional Writing Formats

Lois seemed to startle easily from the sound of the bear growling toy.

Lois was startled and frightened by the sound of the loud music.

Lois had no 'startle response' to the fire alarm.

Lois covers her ears when she is startled by the toilet flushing.

Lois was startled by the sound of the air conditioner.

Materials Responses

Written Example

Gavin does not understand how to use classroom materials.

Optional Writing Formats

Gavin had difficulty with the block building materials and started to throw the blocks at other children.

Gavin does not use materials appropriately and tends to scatter them on the floor.

Gavin tends to put many classroom materials in his mouth and does not use them appropriately.

Gavin did not interact with materials appropriately and would throw toys at other children.

Gavin tried to put the paintbrush in his mouth and did not understand how to use the materials.

Inappropriate Responses

Written Example

Jacob behaved badly at daycare.

Optional Writing Formats

Jacob had a tantrum when asked to stop throwing the blocks.

Jacob started to scream when the teacher approached him at the center activity.

Jacob is not consistently compliant with directions and sometimes ignores the requests.

Jacob does not recognize common dangers and has been observed to take off if not closely supervised.

Jacob responded inappropriately by breaking the toy when offered a choice.

Repetitive Responses

Written Example

Tyrell just plays with the same toy repetitively.

Optional Writing Formats

Tyrell repetitively spins the wheels on the car.

Tyrell lines up many objects in a repetitive and ritualistic manner.

Tyrell likes to fill and dump the truck toy in a repetitive ritual.

Tyrell was observed to say the phrase 'let's go" repeatedly during the art activity.

Tyrell moved the car back and forth repetitively during the lesson.

Changing Routine Response

Written Example

Sophia gets upset when routines are changed.

Optional Writing Formats

Sophia does not respond well when there is a slight change of routine.

Sophia struggles to understand 'why' a routine is changed or something is out of order.

Sophia is often distracted and does not understand changes taking place in the classroom routine.

Sophia tantrums when a classroom routine is changed.

Sophia became angry when the new activity was presented.

Boundary Responses

Written Example

Edward does whatever he wants in preschool with no boundaries.

Optional Writing Formats

Edward was asked to sit in a chair, but crawled under the teacher's desk.

Edward ran out the door when a visitor entered the room.

Edward is very busy and he knocked all the painting supplies on the floor as he ran to the puzzle center.

Edward pulled the toys off the shelves and started to break the toys in a destructive manner.

Edward has difficulty with boundaries and climbed on the teacher's desk.

CHAPTER 9

❖

Autism Report Recommendations

The recommendations section can be helpful for two main reasons. First, parents can see what the next steps for working with the child will be. Second, professionals can view and skim the written autism report to see what the direction of the previous therapist was thinking and how these interactions work with the present evaluation or teaching situation. There can be a variety of recommendations related to the communication are which can include verbal responses, eye contact and social greetings. The recommendation may be important to describe a relationship between the child's delays and abilities with the child's skills to function in practical settings. These functional skills may involve writing about how the child requests items, initiates interactions and participates with other children. The recommendations can direct staff what the next steps will be in helping the child. Additional autism recommendations can explore play and social interaction experiences as well as sensory experiences. Finally, there are many autism recommendations that could focus on practice, monitoring and specialized autism instruction. A monitoring recommendation may be needed to some children when further testing may be warranted in some situations. Some children with autism many be recommended for specialized autism programs with heavy levels of supervision, while other children may need very limited support or even consultation as they function fairly well in a general education setting. These written autism report recommendations can benefit school staff, parents and most importantly the child's educational future.

Social Greeting Recommendations

Written Example

Peter needs to learn to respond to social greetings.

Optional Writing Formats

Peter would benefit in learning to respond to farewell greetings.

It is recommended that Peter be introduced to various forms of social greetings ('hi or bye') and given practice opportunities in the preschool setting.

Peter would benefit from more opportunities to practice using social greetings with puppet games and oral language experiences.

Peter would benefit from speech and language services to increase functional communication in using social greetings.

Peter does not understand how to use social greetings and just walks away when leaving the room.

Communication Recommendations

Written Example

Marley would benefit from more communication with others.

Optional Writing Formats

Speech and language services are recommended to help Marley with functional communication skills.

Marley's lack of communication skills needs to be addressed with speech and language services.

Marley's language delay interferes with her ability to communicate in social situations and speech and language services are recommended.

Marley's significant language delays and the presence of autism needs to be addressed in the preschool setting.

Communication goals are needed to support Marley's delays in functional communication.

Eye Contact Recommendations

Written Example

James needs to be encouraged to make more eye contact.

Optional Writing Formats

James needs to be provided opportunities to coordinate eye contact with looking at another person.

It is recommended that James use more eye contact to direct another person's attention to an object.

James could benefit from opportunities to use more eye contact when spoken to in a group.

It is recommended that James be provided experiences to 'show' items to others as a way of increasing eye contact.

James' parents are encouraged to make eye contact with him in the home setting.

Verbal Response Recommendations

Written Example

George needs to learn to give verbal answers to questions.

Optional Writing Formats

George would benefit from oral language experiences to increase his verbal responses.

It is recommended that George obtain speech and language services to direct his vocalizations to others.

George needs more opportunities to increase his verbal skills as he was inconsistent in using verbal responses during the preschool observation.

George would benefit from encouragement to vocalize his wants and needs.

George needs support and language opportunities to increase his speaking skills.

Social Interaction Recommendations

Written Example

Diane does not use social interaction skills at preschool and should be encouraged.

Optional Writing Formats

It is recommended that Diane gain more large group experiences to increase her social interaction skills.

Diane needs to be provided opportunities at preschool to increase interaction with other children and participate in turn taking.

Diane would benefit from learning how to request objects from other children in the preschool setting.

It is recommended that Diane increase her use of vocalizations and gestures to obtain and request objects.

Diane needs support and additional opportunities in social interaction situations.

Play Experience Recommendations

Written Example

Frankie needs to participate more in play games at daycare.

Optional Writing Formats

Frankie would benefit from learning to participate in daily play routines for at least three minutes a day.

It is recommended that Frankie play with a variety of objects to increase his pretend play skills.

Frankie would benefit from a preschool structure that engages him in more play experiences.

Frankie needs more reinforcement and encouragement in learning to participate in preschool play routines.

Frankie should be provided new opportunities to gain additional experience participating in play routines.

Autism Sensory Experiences Recommendations

Written Example

Ronnie needs to learn to handle different types of objects.

Optional Writing Formats

Ronnie would benefit from being introduced to a variety of objects with different textures.

Ronnie would benefit from extended opportunities to gain new sensory experiences in the classroom.

Ronnie could be provided additional sensory experiences to broaden his interest in learning new concepts.

Ronnie would benefit from encouragement to participate in new sensory experiences and reinforcement when new sensory tasks are introduced.

Sensory materials should be provided for Ronnie to feel and smell in the classroom setting.

Autism Practice Recommendations

Written Example

Willie needs more practice in the autism classroom.

Optional Writing Formats

Willie would benefit from practice where directions are repeated and his preschool teacher can check for understanding.

Willie may need more practice and additional time when he is introduced to new concepts.

Willie should be given opportunities to practice his social interaction skills with same age peers.

Willie would benefit from small group instruction to practice his oral language skills.

Willie needs more practice opportunities to learn turn taking skills.

Autism Monitoring Recommendations

Written Example

Tim should be monitored in an autism classroom.

Optional Writing Formats

Tim's preschool teacher should monitor him and record his progress and responses from each intervention.

The preschool teacher should monitor Tim's progress and note if testing is needed to address his adaptive skills.

Tim might benefit from preschool enrichment experiences to monitor his social interaction skills.

Tim would benefit from a classroom seating arrangement will the preschool teacher can monitor his aggressive behavior.

Tim needs monitoring as he changes his centers and makes transitions in the classroom.

Autism Specialized Instruction Recommendations

Written Example

Nancy needs to be in an autism classroom.

Optional Writing Formats

Nancy's evaluation results indicate a high probability of autism so a specialized autism class is recommended.

Nancy would benefit from intensive direct instruction to address her autism concerns and increase her awareness in the classroom.

A small specialized autism program would benefit Nancy's attention to task providing more positive reinforcement.

Nancy would benefit from a specialized autism program that would provide a high level of supervision due to her self-injurious type of behavior.

Nancy would certainly receive more teacher support in a highly structured autism classroom.

Recommended Reading For Autism

Peterson, S. (2013). *Is my child autistic or delayed?*

Is My Child Autistic or Delayed? is a resource book geared for parents and professionals to explore autism concerns and developmental delays in children. The book has a parent friendly style and is written in easy to understand language. The book is also focused to help professionals by giving an overview of different autism characteristics. *Is My Child Autistic or Delayed?* attempts to explore the multidisciplinary team approach in the decision making process of whether a child is delayed or has autism characteristics.

Is My Child Autistic or Delayed? is a wonderful beginning resource for parents (and professionals) to start the process of an educational assessment for possible autism concerns and developmental delays.

Is My Child Autistic or Delayed? is available in several options (both print and ebook versions) and was selected for the **Gold Winner in the 2014 eLit Awards** and the **2014 West Mountain Regional Reader Views Book** awards program.

Peterson, S, (2014). *Questionable Autism*

The book *Questionable Autism* is focused on opening talk and discussions about a variety of autism topics from many different viewpoints. Looking at professional, parenting, research and testing issues numerous questions are developed to consider the broad impact of autism topics for both parents and professionals across educational and home settings. Author Susan Louise Peterson weaves her years of experience as an educator and school psychologist in the early childhood field into a full discussion of some of the major issues impacting the field of autism. *Questionable Autism* includes many real world examples and practical experiences related to parenting topics, field issues and general practices in the area of autism. *Questionable Autism* has opened the door for broader discussions of many topics in the field autism.

Index

❖

Afterword

❖

Autism **Report Writing** was written to provide exposure to some of the unique issues of writing reports for children with autism. Written autism reports are so valuable in understanding the child's progress and for making referrals to different agencies with resources to help the child. The autism reports not only determine autism eligibility for special education, but they can include parent input, descriptions of behavioral issues and reporting the observations of the child. Professionals have different educational backgrounds and unique styles of writing so reports will vary in what a school psychologist or special education teacher may emphasize. The most important point is that autism reports need to include a well developed description of the child and contain a detailed explanation of the child's autism characteristics and concerns.

Printed in September 2023
by Rotomail Italia S.p.A., Vignate (MI) - Italy